Book of Pages

David
Whiteland

Ringpull

Ringpull

Published by Ringpull Press
An imprint of Stephen Powell Books Ltd

www.ringpullpress.co.uk

Represented and distributed by
Signature Book Representation Ltd
Sunhouse, 2 Little Peter Street
Manchester M15 4PS
Tel: 0161 8348767

A catalogue record for this title
is available from the British Library
ISBN 1 903376 00 9

Printed and bound in Great Britain
Peterson Printers, South Shields, Tyne & Wear

By the same author:
www.beholder.co.uk

Book of Pages website is
www.bookofpages.com

Quotation from Lao Tsu s Tao Te Ching
by permission of Wildwood House Limited.
Biblical quotation (Ecclesiastes 7:29/30)
from the Jerusalem Bible

The mapper solves her problem by drawing
the rats map on transparent paper.

A journey of a thousand miles begins with a single step.

Jiriki is sweeping it and so, perhaps without him knowing, his journey begins. Sweeping a significant step is much the same as sweeping any other ... it can be more or less dusty than the rest but, whichever, your life is changed.

Even if the monastery were built of ice under a three-sunned sky, the things that happen inside it would be ordinary. As it is, the monastery is built of stone and wood, and if there are three suns then the Abbot has only ever seen them one at a time.

The monks live in the monastery. After all, that is what the word means; it is what the place means. They spend every day doing a series of ordinary things: chopping wood, carrying water, preparing food, tending illness, being still, growing crops, reading speaking, writing, breathing ... Between each day there is sleeping and waking, which is ordinary too. And so each life here is a series of ordinary things. Yet from these ordinary things grows understanding — of respect, discipline, insight, humour, loyalty and love. If all their ingredients are ordinary, perhaps this too is just a series of ordinary things.

Any series of ordinary things is simple. The Abbot, like the abbots before him, chooses to pursue the hidden quality that might reside in simplicity — and leaves most of the revelations that lurk among complexity and its many numbers to the rest of the world. So now he stays here, overseeing the routine and the ordinary.

Pages are ordinary.

When Jiriki gets to the Metropolis, that most modern of habitats, he will meet people who are not familiar with the concept of obedience. They would call it subservience or submission. They don't, as they tell each other, take orders from anybody. It would seem that in the Metropolis this is something of which to be proud. The idea of accepting somebody's direction without question, without demanding an explanation, would be alien indeed. Yet, when the Abbot sends Jiriki on his journey, which is something he is about to do, Jiriki will not question it.

This trust is not blind devotion — it is a necessary part of being receptive to teaching. The monks, as teachers, are concerned with life, and the awareness that comes with it; life cannot be usefully taught or learnt, but it can be discovered. The monks know, and the Abbot knows best, that there is enough to get on with just understanding things without having to understand their explanations as well. Or, to put it another way, the monks' kitchen has several cookbooks in it, but no matter how carefully or diligently you read any or all of them, you will not discover what the food tastes like. To do that, you should stop reading and start eating.

That is not to say, however, that books do not have their worth. Just when Jiriki's mind has learnt to adapt to the rigours of the meditation hall — the clamour of an unexpected chime, the turmoil of an icy cup of water thrown, the curiosity of a feather snapped: all these tricks of his teachers — he is sent into the Metropolis to retrieve a book.

The Abbot, probably for reasons best known to himself, is vague with his description. He simply tells him: "You'll recognise it when you've found it." In fact, there is a system in the Metropolis by which you can find a book just by knowing the number it was given when it was born. Jiriki doesn't know about this system, but the Abbot does, which is one of the reasons he doesn't mention it. He is, after all, an Abbot, not a librarian.

When he leaves for the Metropolis, Jiriki is following the most vague of directions, both geographically (how to get there) and objectively (what to do when he does). Neither of these causes him undue concern. The Abbot appeared to know that Jiriki would find the Metropolis and find the book he has been sent for. Among these monks, appearances are rarely deceptive.

Jiriki learnt to walk long before he knew why it would be useful. In fact, like almost everybody else who learns to walk, he learnt before he'd been taught to learn. Those first few steps were staggeringly pure; because their success was dependent neither on instructional advice nor previous experience. The first walk — it's not really fair to call it a journey — was achieved by moving his feet in response to the immediate requirements. In the Metropolis, that would be called on-line real-time foot control. Those steps

worked for the right reasons. If it wasn't for the fact that the monks practice walking like infants, that would have been the last time he ever walked so well. Jiriki, like the other monks, feels the ground pushing against the soles of his feet when he stands or walks. Whereas, by the time they are tall enough for falling over to be a harmful problem, nearly everybody else is walking solely by conditioning.

So Jiriki is travelling. Travel is the inevitable symptom of a journey, even one like this which starts and ends in the same place.

As he watches his student gradually walk out of sight, the Abbot smiles to himself with a gentle feeling of accomplishment. Now that his preparations are finally complete, he need no longer postpone departure on a long-awaited journey of his own. Wisdom, as he has often told the younger monks, is largely a matter of timing.

LIKE THE SPRINTING TREE

The Metropolis is progressing fast, like the Sprinting Tree.

What has happened there, Jiriki, is what we call progress. Now technology has taken the reins and the pace is ever increasing: more, more, faster, faster! It is a huge mistake. Let me tell you about the Sprinting Tree which, I have come to suspect, was grown purely for the purposes of analogy.

There are no trees in the Metropolis, because we can fabricate shade and oxygen in our own modern ways. But for a number of reasons, none of them particularly compassionate, trees have not escaped the attention of our science. We can correct genetics to get a better shaped tree, to produce fruit that is the right size, shape and colour, and that contains all the right additives. So it is that we could, just as easily, make the Sprinting Tree.

Ordinary trees grow, and they grow towards the sun. But the genetic engineers, for the sake of treekind, created an improved strain: the Sprinting Tree, which didn't just grow towards the sun — it got up and ran towards it.

It's not clear to the genetic engineers what went wrong with the Sprinting Tree. It ought to have been a success; it had an impressive turn of speed, and could cover great distances tirelessly. Infinite improvements on being rooted to the ground and just straining towards the light! But from time to time they find one that has finally died, lying toppled at the end of its trail of mighty, bounding rootprints. When they come to examine it, they always discover the same disappointing result: it's nothing more than, well, wood: the same stuff as all of its motionless predecessors.

Perhaps if they had given it more knees or made the legs longer, it would have gone fast enough to make a difference.

Or perhaps that's not it at all.

5

When I was a small boy I took it upon myself to be an explorer. I made maps of all the streets and alleys I played in, and went on forays further and further out into the unknown twists and turns of the Metropolis. I would get into trouble for straying so far afield — I'd sneak off when I was supposed to be playing nearby and sneak back just in time to come in. Well, of course, I don't remember the details of those forays now, except for the one when it rained ... rained so suddenly and for so long, when I was a long, unallowed distance away, that although I ran back through the streets as fast as only an urgent boy can, feet flapping, I couldn't pretend that I hadn't been away. Oh I got scolded for that! I wasn't allowed out alone for months and months. And I, of course, got terribly upset because my maps were getting out of date without my regular patrols.

Naturally, after my release I crept off more than ever. My excuses and disappearances became even more devious, but always at the back of my mind I knew that I hadn't overcome the problem of getting caught out by the rain. I suppose I must have become fascinated by it; I ended up asking one of the street-workers how to stay dry. I'd probably seen him working before and after rainstorms. It occurs to me now that he most likely stood in a doorway while they lasted, but I was a child then, and such a mundane explanation would

have escaped me. He looked at me with a strange grin, which, at the time, impressed me enormously because of the small number of teeth it contained, and told me: "I walk between raindrops."

I remember practicing in a hut nearby which had a leaky roof. I could walk from end to end of it weaving among the big drips. It was a good start. Just a question of being aware of all the drops, where they were, and how far advanced their fall was. All through my schooldays I thought about learning to walk between raindrops. It was only when they were over that I realised it was something I was never going to be taught. Among so much useless rubbish, such a precise, beautiful skill had been left out.

So I decided to discover it for myself. I've spent a lifetime walking out when it rains, and contemplating the problem when it doesn't. I had to leave the Metropolis; people thought I was mad, and, besides, I used to get knocked down in the traffic. But it has been a worthwhile way to spend a life. Can you imagine how it feels to be aware of every raindrop that falls around you? I no longer have to imagine. I can walk between raindrops.

Of course, I get as wet as you do — I don't walk between *all* of them — but *now* I understand enough to know that staying dry was never important.

All my possessions forgot I was their owner. It happened abruptly — one night I was woken by the intruder alarm ringing, and the lights pulsing on and off in bewilder-mode. I stumbled up, setting off microsirens on everything I touched. In the end I fled because it was getting noisy and I guessed the police would burst in any moment; and, besides, I knew that in domestic complexes like mine the choking gas hits the air-con ten minutes after the first alarms are triggered. Anything I tried to grab started up its anti-theft whine or attention strobe. So I pulled on my shoes and made a run for it, and left it all behind.

By the time I hit the street below, the first police agent had already blown the front door out. I was lucky to get away. You can understand I couldn't go back until I could convince my possessions they were mine, otherwise you can be sure I would be prosecuted for the theft of every single item, as well as trespassing. And breaking the window I jumped out of.

It seemed pretty obvious that my ID card had failed and wasn't sending out the right number, so I had to try to fix that up. I'd heard of the old traditionalists in the outskirts who can wire together overrides and patches, so I found my way to them. Eventually, one gave me this faker-box: punch in an ID number, he said, and it sends out the right signal.

Well, that was a number of years ago; I've not been counting. You can hear that my shoes are still bleeping — they still don't recognise me. The problem was that I couldn't remember my number — I'm not sure that I *ever* could. But I knew that if I started low enough and just worked through them all, then eventually I would hit the right one. Every night, before I go to sleep, I have to remember what number I've got to, so I can start up again the next day; so each day I work through the next batch of numbers, being very careful not to miss any out.

One day, you see, my shoes will be silent and I will be able to return.

They'd have you believe that flying's all about Split-S turns, Immelmann loops and stall speeds. All that stuff up in the sky — yes, that's flying. And the freedom of flight, yes, that's real too. When you have felt what it's like to have such freedom of movement, it's painful to have to walk upon the predetermined, sticky ground ever again. But these are just personal experiences. Flying is bigger than this: it's an immense solution to one of the major problems of living in a physical world.

Can you see what I mean? We have to move about, and we have spent an evolution learning to do it under the simple and awesome constraints of physical obstacles. We learnt to swim, to climb, to build tracks and to dig tunnels. Then, suddenly, we learnt to fly — and we rose up above the problem and all its obstacles. I call this an immense solution. It is an immense solution to the problem of destination. I often dream that there are other immense solutions to our other limitations, and I wonder what judder of insight would be needed to glance them. But that's something else again.

Maps are just snapshots of the destination problem. I mean, you look at one to see what obstacles are in the way of your destination, and you plan ways to overcome them. But ordinary maps are maps of real-space; they tell you very little that you couldn't see for yourself (if it wasn't for the limitations of human eyesight), and they don't actively help you find a solution. It's not interesting to be shown that the Destination is very close to Here if there is no direct path between the two. Destination problem-space is different. For example, if you are at an airfield, then in a map of problem-space all the other airfields are close by because they are easy to get to, whereas your monastery, up in the mountains, would seem very remote. But problem-space is always shifting and changing. Suppose we have to close the runway for repairs — the problem-space would alter, and the cluster of other airfields would move further away ... and all the while, the whole thing pulses to the rhythms of timetables and seat availability.

Well, it's a curious thing, watching problem-space. Since the advent of the Immense Solution, everywhere is much, much closer. Naturally, as the mechanics of transport constantly improve — faster planes, wider roads, bigger engines — the whole wide world, in problem-space, is shrinking. It's nowhere near as wide as it used to be. A growing number of people in a shrinking world: no wonder the world seems overcrowded.

Flying through the air, crossing the sky like a bird is something that Jiriki has never done before. It is one of the more outlandish and visible abilities that technology bestows upon its subjects. Up until now, if it was altitude that Jiriki wanted, he would have had to climb up the mountain. That in itself can be exhilarating, of course, but not as astonishing as cutting through the air, supported on borrowed wings instead of sandalled feet. So as he approached the airfield, he was rather looking forward to being carried in such an exciting manner into the Metropolis.

The monks are warned time and time again of the unreliability of looking forward to things which are only expected, not experienced. And Jiriki's experience of flight, that most fantastic of human dreams, turns out to be somewhat different from that which he had expected.

Not because of the enforced loitering that he and other passengers were obliged to indulge in before they were allowed to board the aircraft. Having to endure a period of inactivity is not as demanding for a monk who is used to quiet and still meditation as it seems to be for modern people, who accurately while away each minute, and every single second, with frustration.

No. It is because when it comes to flying, all the tell-tale symptoms have been designed away. There is no rush of air, no giddying feeling of acceleration, no freedom. Jiriki sits in a crowded room, long and narrow, has drinks and light refreshments, gets entertained: all sorts of things, none of them admitting to the activity of flight. And while he and the others sit diligently in their comfortable seats, waiting to be allowed to leave, outside — somehow or other — the airfield is changed into a huge concrete airport in the midst of the great Metropolis. A mammoth task, and one which not surprisingly takes several hours to complete.

EXITS ↑ ↑
↑ CHANNELS 4 AND 61
BAGGAGE CLAIM THRESHOLD NOW
8 MINUTES TO INCINERATION

The first time people see something new, they think they have enough information to pass judgement on it. Despite a never-ending supply of evidence to the contrary, the reliability of first impressions is seldom questioned.

Perhaps, though, those first impressions are not so unreasonable after all. It could be that the first time somebody looks at something is the last time they manage to remain uninvolved by familiarity with it. So it is with Jiriki's first impression of the Metropolis — a first impression which a designer, or team of designers, or designing machine has meticulously created.

The Metropolis airport arrival terminal is being deliberate when it dwarfs its guests with its humbling magnitude. The floors are so tough and shiny that they are resilient to any mark or trace which your presence may have made. The doors are always flung apart — and they are huge enough and defiant enough that you have to believe that, were they to shut, they would not open again just for small human beings. The details are kept to a minimum: invisible cracks hide between the featureless slabs; there are no devices or fixtures that might be on your own scale. You are in the Metropolis, and you are tiny.

Transparency is a remarkable quality for any material to possess. Not least because there is — or so it seems to Jiriki — something fundamentally curious about things being there that you can see through. After all, a popular side effect of something being anywhere is that you can see it. Telling the difference between transparent and invisible is an acquired skill. Until you've practiced, you can't make the choice between looking through and looking at.

I can't tell you where to find a book! Don't be foolish! That's not what teller means! I tell people how much they're worth. And I can't tell you that because you haven't got any accounts — not even the usual credit account opened at birth by the midwife — and there are no machines that are willing to vouch for you. If someone wants to know how many consumables they are entitled to have each month, or how big a fine they can afford to pay, I can calculate it and I'll tell them. But look, if you won't give me machine-readable ID, how can I begin to work out what you're worth?

It's unlikely that someone like you would have much value anyway. The absolute detail of actual amounts of money is mostly irrelevant when oscillating prices and interest and deals make costs so variable. The important thing is whether or not you can afford the things you need or want; and that depends on what kind of person you are, what you do, your education and upbringing, who you know, that sort of stuff. Before, in the early days of money, the quantity you had — your wealth — measured this. Wealthy people accrued large amounts, poor or unreliable people only had small amounts. But now, of course, we can determine (from this month's records of your activities — assuming you had any) how wealthy you are directly, so we no longer need to rely on the old system of counting up money.

Listen — let me tell you a tale: you're not the first person to come here with bad ID. I had someone once shuffle up and pass me an ID that looked damaged, maybe scorched or acid-bitten. Well, these things happen, industrial accidents and so on. I guessed the person had been damaged or scarred themselves, what with the face visor and power-assisted gloves. So, anyway, I put the card in and kicked-off the calculation. I glanced up at the reader screen: the card was so badly wiped that the only identifying criterion was "HUMAN". Everything else was blank. But by then it was too late to interrupt. So the calculation took in the movements of *all* people, it considered everybody's activity and status, it weighed up their debts and credits and allowed for the amounts in transmission. It knew how much the machines were holding and how much was left distributed among the people.

The calculation took less than a minute to conclude that the humans, just at that instant, were worth nothing at all. The customer nodded courteously, before turning precisely around and walking methodically away. I remember listening to the curious sound of his — or her — joints hissing and those metal boots clicking against the floor; by the time I realised that I still had the ID card, the figure had disappeared into the crowd. I didn't call out. I think I threw the card away, quickly.

For the convenience of machines, presumably, people trade in numbers. The numbers are supposed to represent units of money. It's become an archaic visualisation, but it's sufficiently useful that people stick with it.

Money in itself was always going to be interesting. A good coin is worth what it represents; gold has, in the past, been popular, but among hungry people biscuits are a reasonable alternative. But numbers: well, what kind of population trustfully trades in numbers alone? Perhaps a society of mathematicians. Or, more likely, a society of digital machines.

A founding principle of money is that it is versatile. Almost anything can be converted to anything else via the formless form of money. So coinage and notes quickly become tokens, whose only value lies with their potential. Money is one of the most abstract things you could ever hope to jangle in your pocket. If what is needed is a scale of representation that is versatile and convenient, you don't stop with metal discs for very long; numbers do nicely instead. Universal and unencumbering — at last, money freed from the material world. Here is a society where materialism has transcended into mysticism. Before, you couldn't take it with you; now, it's gone on ahead.

And this money moves fast: not moving in position, since it has none, but changing form and quantity and ownership. Faster than the human eye — passing among machines that deal in it, work with it, communicate with it. Machines that, quite reasonably, have their own accounts, and have good credit. (A machine is, necessarily, deterministic and not liable to most of the deviations that make humans such very bad credit risks). Machines that can, if so configured, be revenue earning.

Any flavour, any texture, available while—U—wait: until now, Jiriki had never known urgency so great that there's no time to spell "you" with all three letters. This food is unnecessarily fast — nobody here is going to faint if they don't eat in the next 60 seconds. But people don't come to be nourished. Most are pulled in by the subtle barbs of advertising. The craving for food used to be a response to hunger: now it's a response to marketing.

Jiriki, being a stranger here and a little uncertain of the proper form, doesn't order fast enough. He's jostled and complained at while he tries to understand how this bewildering choice can be reduced down into something he can eat. There's more variety of food and flavour here than he has ever encountered in his life — and it's all configurable, in any colour and taste he wants, and all neatly, corporately served in germ-free plastic containers. He simply can't make his mind up against such a meaningless spread of possibilities — he ends up pointing hurriedly at an illuminated menu board. The result is something which is as mysterious to him as a root vegetable dug out of non-sterile earth would be to any of his fellow diners. He looks down into a cup labelled "thick-O-shake": whatever it is, it *is* thick, and sometime in its history a machine almost certainly did shake it.

The rush and urgency with which Jiriki is surrounded is a novelty to him. It's a little unnerving — he expects there to be some underlying emergency justifying it all. But there is no emergency here. It might be that when the modern world is in such a hurry to deliver, it is because what it has to offer is not worth waiting for.

High technology, despite its deceptive complexity, has never really soared much above the primeaval soup of two-state devices (light bulb ON or light bulb OFF) from which it ungracefully emerged. When all is said and done, the thing it's still best at doing is saying either one thing or the other; on or off, true or false, yes or no. Yet somehow this tiny, seemingly trivial ability has been granted far more prestige than it could ever deserve, and as a result, technology now has an almost total monopoly on the business of Yes-ing and No-ing. In practical terms, the most prevalent forms of these are "Yes you can" and "No you can't".

Perhaps this would be of no great concern if the recipients of such binary permissions could choose to ignore them. But in the disturbing field of control — which is what Jiriki is witnessing here — the authorising machines are careful to issue their opinions only to other devices, devices which have no compunction but to obey. Thus, when a machine says "No you can't", or "Access Denied", or even "Please try later", it does not consider for a moment whether or not you will take its advice. When it sends the signal to a door, or a powered shutter, or a high-voltage security plate and liquidizer, you are not being informed of the machine's decision, you are being controlled by it. None of these systems ever have a "Beg-

to-differ" button, because that's not part of what a modern "no" really means.

The girl, like everyone else, has her four personal public-access numbers, which allow entry to all public pedestrian capillaries — it's useful to move off the main routes, especially when you are being pursued, as is the case in this instance. Her numbers are sixteen, and eight, and four, and one (some rather beautiful numbers, in fact, although she, like most people, doesn't have an eye for such things). When the pad asks for the checksum — the total of them all — despite the obvious answer, it opts to deny. She gets the NO of a door that remains unambiguously closed even to increasingly urgent attempts to open it. It's a malfunction, from the pragmatic point of view, and the machine is wrong; a terrifying possibility, and one which no technologically-informed mind would ever stoop to consider.

So the door, despite having been asked quite desperately, refuses to open, and the girl's burly pursuers do catch her and drag her off. She doesn't go quietly — until they drug her with a press-on tranquillizer pad of course. In fact, she shouts those numbers, again and again, to those who care to listen. Jiriki hears it, because unlike every other passer-by in the Metropolis, he has yet to master the shameful art of remaining uninvolved.

Two things lead to a society like the one in the Metropolis: the spread of ubiquitous technology, and a culture of ferocious litigation. People no longer act out of social conscience — in an earlier era of the development of the Metropolis, you could get sued for trying to be kind, which is a certain way to find a cure for kindness. But now, the people who help you up if you stumble are not doing so out of compassion, they are summoned members of society, and it's their job.

If you are unfortunate enough to find yourself in a situation in which you are unable to cope without assistance — trapped under the wreckage of an transport accident, for example — the people of the Metropolis will do all they can: they will alert the system. They can't get more involved than

that because of the inevitability — it's no longer merely a risk — of litigation. It's very hard to pull someone out of wreckage without traumatising them later in life, especially if they have good lawyers.

Jiriki, assuming quite rightly that abductions are not condoned by the unfamiliar society which he is visiting, attempts to report the event he has just witnessed using the part of the system which seems to be here especially for that purpose. But society is not available to those who cannot prove their status as paid-up members, and instead of summoning help, he is, albeit unwittingly, merely drawing attention to himself. The machine, fearing that it is being tampered with, will call the police.

Well, I guess you have nothing to say for yourself. I don't know what charge to aim at you first: Intent to use Fraudulent Credit (on account of you carrying no credit) or Compromising the Integrity of All Personal Data Stores (on account of you carrying no ID). Or maybe Intent to Cause Grievous Bodily Damage to a Public Machine. You ridiculous troublemakers are only any use when the arrest quotas are low. We've got better things to do than go rounding up people who get their kicks from being unlisted you know.

There's no excuse for having nothing better to do than wasting my time. There are plenty of leisure facilities and entertainment plazas in this zone. Or maybe you want to work, right? OK — join the Police. You might pass as serious if you wore some padding to beef you up a bit. Some of the small guys do make a living. A lot of them are snipers, or at the least knife-throwers. What about you, eh? Is the stick dangerous?

You can apply for your personal Police franchise at any of the police bunkers. You just have to show them that you've got money in an account somewhere — we can't have people doing this because they need the money, of course. Then you get the pick of any of the equipment, for a returnable deposit. The badge comes free, but you have to put money down for the heavy gear.

And then most of the time you're your own boss. There's no corruption within the organisation — a common problem with enforcing bodies — because there is no organisation. Just well-motivated individuals, like myself. It's self-policing too; everybody watches their own back because it's double score for taking in a police officer. For the bigger operations, the jobs which require units instead of individuals, the logistics and tactics are all handled by the Command and Control Systems. So from time to time you do have to follow orders — but they are output from a machine, not commands from somebody else, so it's not as if you're inferior to anyone.

Anyway, I'm not here to recruit you, I'm here because a machine reported you for failing to produce ID, and I happened to be near enough to come and bring you in.

Imprisonment itself — the denial of the freedom to roam and the freedom to choose your surroundings — is an unpleasant thing. But, more often than not, before the loss of freedom even becomes noticeable, people fail to cope with the isolation. Put them in a place where there is no screen to show the latest entertainment, no speakers thrusting popular music into every gap, not even anybody with whom to be irritable, and they will probably go mad.

There are some exceptions. Put a quiet monk from the mountains, one used to sitting still in silences disturbed only by the tell-tale heartbeat of self, into any sort of isolation, and you may as well throw a fish into water. Or, the Abbot might have preferred to suggest, a stone into sand. Sometimes fish tend to thrash around a bit.

Time is a difficult thing to deal with in its purest form. In time, like space, the human mind is good at remembering the landmarks, but not the expanses between them. Perhaps this is because time itself is a slippery substance resistant to being held in the grip of thought; or perhaps it is quite an ordinary thing, but one which the untrained mind finds repulsively taboo. Either theory explains the desperation with which humans will invent distractions for themselves, filling every moment with an event — the beat of a synthesizer, the scream of an exploding actor — so that they might run one event into the other, and expose nothing of that line of unnerving time on which those events sit. The irony, of course, is that the events are inconsequential in the extreme, and most lives, viewed as the temporal landscapes they really are, have the dire architecture of funfairs and theme parks.

Meanwhile, Jiriki sits quite still, and has the reassuring experience of time passing in the same unambiguously simple way that it always does, even on mountains.

MISSING NUMBER

Mathematics is a hard thing to love. It has the unfortunate habit, like a rude dog, of turning its most unfavourable side towards you when you first make contact with it. That unfavourable side is arithmetic, and most people never really get the legacy of that initial encounter off their fingers — which is where counting starts, and for most, where it remains. Perhaps such an unwelcoming exterior serves a useful purpose — it deters casual visitors from stumbling into the awesome discoveries that lie beyond. Mathematics: you can get lost in such a beautiful place; unlike the real world, it has a purity that makes even simulated reality seem grubby; it is devoid of arbitrary construction in the same way the real world used to be, before people learnt to tear natural things down and throw unnatural things up. It is the best wilderness in which to retreat, to fast, to search for enlightenment. It is, paradoxically, about the only place where you really can take refuge from the modern world's unrelenting barrage of numbers. But only mathematicians, and the various subspecies and half-breeds thereof, go there, which might be another reason why it is so unpopular with almost everyone else.

Jiriki's training is not in mathematics; he has neither an aversion nor an affinity to it. He's more familiar with the absence of numbers that arises from a still mind that neither counts nor calculates. But the numbers which the girl shouted out have reverberated in his mind in a manner strangely familiar to him, yet in a most unmathematical way. They seem to be pointing to a number he thought he knew, but now, when he thinks towards it, he cannot find. It's a pleasant enigma for him, because he is not afraid of the sensation of nothingness, as it is something his teachers gently acquainted him with during his (uncounted) hours of meditation.

So he takes the beads, which are actually nutritional pills for the convenience of detainees like himself awaiting prosecution. He builds a pile of sixteen, then eight, then another four, and then one more bead, adding as he does so. But every time, as that single bead drops from his fingers to meet the others, his mind cannot settle on the sum: the beads are all there, but the number isn't. No doubt about it: a number is missing.

THE MAGICIAN

Out of thin air (the kind of air favoured by magicians): a ticket! Come to my next show — when I've paid my fine, or served my sentence. This happens to me from time to time ... I find myself here, because some machine-eye or camera sees me make a coin disappear before a crowd, and the crime-matching algorithms pick such a thing up as "embezzlement". It's tiresome, but I'll probably get a penalty which will be added to all the others, and taken off my credit.

How can you tell whether something's missing or whether it's not? Now you see it, now you don't! Now you follow, now you're lost! Easily baffled, easily fooled ... ah, but no — I see there's more to you than meets the eye. How interesting. I think we should talk.

When I make a card disappear (pick a card — any card!), or when I pull a silk scarf from your ear (choose a colour — any colour you want!) it is simply magic. Absolutely, simply magic — nothing to it, no great mystery, no special powers. Let me tell

you, because I think you already know: it is always just a simple trick.

It's so simple, it's astonishing. So simple that nobody around here can begin to understand it. It took me ten years to teach my fingers how to do these simple things. Then another ten years to do the same things backwards. Three cups and one ball; one hat and no rabbit; what could be simpler than that? Unbelievable!

Do you see, Jiriki, the simplest things are the hardest ones to spot? People are baffled by my magic because they try to understand it. Their understanding thrives on explanation and complexity. They think there is something here to work out, but they will never find it because there isn't. You see, the modern world is so complex that simplicity can slip through the gaps. Practice is simple; a flick of the wrist is simple; one coin that looks a lot like all the others is simple; these things defy explanation.

Pick a card, any card. Might as well use the time wisely!

THE ANGEL OF BLAME

The Metropolis runs on electricity and blame. Electricity stirs the machines; it animates the technology. Blame is the power that drives the systems; it animates the people. Just as the machines have their wires and cables and ducts, so the organisations have their channels of blame. Teams, departments, companies: all are built around their complex hierarchies of blame.

Not so long ago, it used to be the case that when I appeared before someone, they were afraid. A visit from the Angel of Blame used to be the most fearful thing that they could imagine. I was, more often than not, a portent of financial ruin — and in a world where they no longer needed to fear disease, hunger or injury, financial ruin was about as scary as things could get. I would hover above the wreckage of tragedy and wield my finger not just to rebuke, but to redistribute the wealth.

For a while I was the champion of the aggrieved, and people respected me and my mission.

But since then, things have changed. Now, people have been wholly subsumed by their hierarchies of blame — the systems themselves have taken over. It's hard for me to find anyone who is really responsible for their own actions. There is always some larger factor, a mitigating circumstance or past influence which means the system absorbs the blame instead of the individual. I can't, with any confidence, point at anyone any more and say "your fault".

Of course, if people can no longer be blamed, I could always pick on the systems that have freed them of their responsibility. I could end up just waving vaguely at this modern society. Something has gone wrong: what happened to stern, old-fashioned pointing? What happened to blame? What happened to responsibility?

THE PROSECUTOR

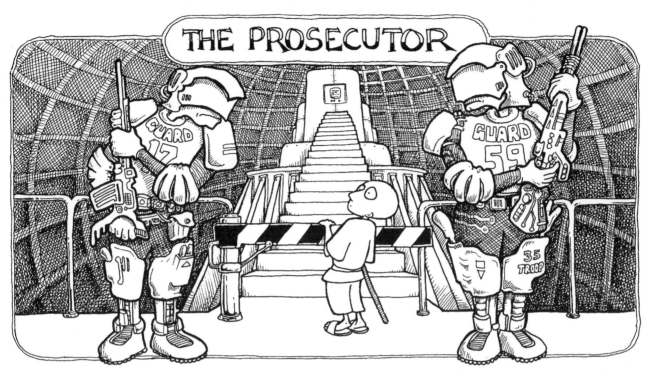

Sometimes machines change the way things are done to the extent that the new method or system is completely different from the old way of doing things.

Sometimes machines fall into line and just implement the old way, which remains unchanged — except, of course, that the humans are removed from the system.

Sometimes the machines' attempts to be involved are resisted, and the humans continue with their own methods.

Actually, the last of these three cases is misleading, since it is invariably an early stage of one of the other two.

The Prosecutor, before which Jiriki is about to appear, is an example of a machine that faithfully implemented an existing system. It simply streamlined it by removing the humans. This was one of the two improvements it was designed to make, and it succeeded. What makes it unusual is that, although it superseded a considerable body of people, the actual system that was left turned out to be very straightforward. The Prosecutor, in fact, is a very small machine. Its large and imposing casing was added afterwards, for psychological reasons. The guards were an afterthought too. They are not there, as is widely believed, to prevent sabotage. They keep people far enough away to prevent them from tapping its hollow exterior.

The Prosecutor's purpose is to pass sentences on criminals. The human system it replaced was a large and complex affair, of which judges and juries were a well-known part. A typical sentence, or term of punishment, used to depend on a number of factors: things like the oratory skills of the lawyers, the disposition and composition of the jury, the strategies of either side, and the ever-growing collection of precedents. And the whole process was a long one.

Now things are different. The Prosecutor has a list of charges, their accompanying penalties, and the percentage of cases, under the old system, that were 'sent down'. So, on a monthly basis, it accurately and speedily commits exactly the same proportion of offenders to punishment. The new result is — by definition — statistically identical to the old. And because the Prosecutor is able to pass sentence using simple, well-understood probability, it does not need to take into account things like the persuasiveness of the prosecution, or the facts of the case. Its results are impervious to bias and, hence, injustice; which is important, because this is the other improvement over the old system that it was introduced to make.

Jiriki is routine: he is to be identified. He also gets a fine (dated to be taken seconds after his credit account is created) for breaches of the Freedom Act (Identification), and Attempting to Use a Public Machine Whilst Not a Member of the Public. Prosecution ends.

The identification process involves detailed analysis of his body, his mind and, of course, his credit potential. It takes several pages.

Hold it there, right there; no blinking while I get this right... You might not realise it, but you're in front of an artist here. Always striving for the perfect picture — the one that captures the essence of the subject, that really gets to the core of their being. It's not easy, you know: all these settings and levels to get right, angles and depths to consider, each factor precisely interacting with all the others in a matrix of delicate complexity, where precision and craftsmanship is everything. And afterwards, I press this little button which sorts the blurs out, tidies up the colours and straightens everything up. So actually it's perfect art every time.

Anyway, back to work: this is needed for your records. You don't know when or why anyone will be looking at them, but you can be sure that at any given time, somebody will be; a detective looking for suspects, an advertiser looking for targets. For this reason it's generally considered prudent to adopt the expression which you consider least likely to draw attention to yourself. I don't recommend smiling.

MEASURABLY BETTER

Measurement is to technology what faith used to be to religion. Without it we would still be floundering in a mire of inaccuracy and vagueness. Instead, we have conquered the world because we have measured it. If there is anything we want to understand, we need only to turn our instruments upon it and take enough readings — to as many decimal places as we require — to know everything about it.

The tools we use, like the mathematics we employ, are impartial. They return absolute answers ... numbers that are unsullied by human subjectivity. We get such a pure description of the world: facts that are unquestionable, absolute, and definitively correct. Measurements provide all the proof that any disbeliever in the divinity of science could require.

There will come a time when the precision of our measurements can no longer be refined. That day of Ultimate Resolution is closer than you think! The new world is already being revealed: everything our measurements illuminate is shown to us with startling clarity. Where uncertainty and ambiguity used to dwell, we bring quantity and scale:

Wisdom — elusive before, is now encapsulated with IQ points!

Success — previously vague, is now definitively shown by Credit Rating!

Disaster — formerly so hard to rank, is now easily scaled in the Loss-of-Life unit!

These breakthroughs (and there are many more) proclaim the dawn of our new realisation: only that which can be measured can be said to exist. And so, as we shed the clutter of the coarse resolution of our ancestors' knowledge, a clearer, more truthful world emerges.

The Final Measurement — after which nothing remains to be measured, and no more detail can be drawn out of our completely precise measuring machinery — is near at hand! We know, because we can already measure the accuracy of our measurements, so we can project ahead. Measurement is the highest form of technology, and its ascension is almost complete.

If you live without measurements, then you live in ignorance. For example: how high above sea-level is your monastery? You see? You don't have the facts with which to answer even the simple questions. How can you begin to make sense of the world with so little information?

24

In such a thoroughly technological world, it is something of a discrepancy that the humans have remained so biological. Their lives are massively interwoven with the machines around them, but evolution — despite considerable encouragement in some genetics laboratories — has refused to incorporate even the most basic of digital electronics.

So the humans in the Metropolis are not complete without some further, artificial artefact. Each one carries their ID, a circuit-card which identifies them uniquely; there are a lot of people in the Metropolis, and the machines have to be able to tell them apart. Circuit cards are far more efficient — and much less arbitrary — than names, which are the outrageously primitive alternative.

Of course, this particular application of technology, namely providing a statistically unique identification for every individual, has arisen out of necessity. But even allowing for excuses of scale, the fact remains there are now members of this population who are so unremarkable that it is only their ID which makes them unique.

Meanwhile, Jiriki has been measured and tested and analysed, and his data has been deposited within the databanks of the Metropolis. He is given his slightly pathetic, slightly crucial card, and he is a member of the public, whether he wanted to be or not. He starts in debt, of course, because he has old fines to pay, as well as back-dated birth tax — and all those tests (biological, mental and fiscal) don't come cheap either. If it wasn't for credit, he would be grounded already. As it is, the system's analysis of his profile concludes that this individual has been under-exposed to the levels of comfort to which modern humans are required to become accustomed. He is to be held in a comfort zone until his quota has been fulfilled and his assimilation into the general public, probably in several years' time, will be truly complete.

Are you sitting comfortably, Jiriki? The system brought you here, because your test results showed you would best be suited to a long spell in this environment. I've been here most of my life, and I fully intend to die comfortably unless my credit expires first. So I know what I'm talking about and you should pay attention, because I'm going to tell you about comfort: the comfort that shaped this place and the society within it.

When you imagine what motivated great people to do the things which made them allegedly great, what springs to mind? Peace, love and honour? Ambition, greed and revenge? Perhaps even fear, hate and hunger? They can all be, in their own time and circumstance, raw and noble and tremendous. But in fact, all they do is inspire the imagination: for, despite what we like to think, these things did not mould the world that we live in today. The disappointing truth is that the modern world, far from being carved by such passions, was eroded into its current shape by the overwhelming undertow of the power of comfort.

Humans may have aspired to greatness in their talk or in their dreams, but the only life most of them ever genuinely craved was an easier one. So through the ages they worked, researched, and more than occasionally struggled, paradoxically, to find ways to make their lives more comfortable. But

comparatives never make good targets: if you want an easy life, you'll know when you've got it, but if you set your sights on an easier life, then there will always be further to go. With technologically image-enhanced hindsight, it's clear that this is just the kind of never-ending regression that should never be allowed into the uncritical, slavish hands of machines. But that, of course, is exactly what happened here — and as soon as technology was invited to aid in the descent into comfort, the fate of humans was irrevocably sealed.

So, for a tiny example, we have made remote controls because the effort of reaching out with a pressing finger is too much. Yet our weary fingers have ancestors that once dug a well or made a bicycle because half a day was too far to reach out for water. And now, we won't buy the wrong sort of remote controller, because it doesn't fit our hand carressingly enough, or because we have to push the buttons too firmly. Our changes — in everything — stopped being improvements long ago: now they are irresistible shuffles towards the inevitable rigor mortis of Utopian comfort.

You should not underestimate the power of comfort. To our everlasting discredit, we owe our utter dependency on technology, and the conclusive design of our stagnant society, to our inability to resist it.

It's common for a book to have at least one villain. There are a great many villains in the Metropolis, and competition between them is fierce indeed. As a result, this one, like any of the others that could have been chosen, is occupied with full-time villainy. In the modern world, organised crime and misbehaviour is a very demanding business. Its captains don't have time to appear more than fleetingly in books — hence this single, posed illustration, and the understanding that he will remain anonymous throughout, since he survives the book. He does not get his come-uppance, because this is not that sort of fiction, and his operation is in no way jeopardised by his appearance in print, now or hereafter.

It would be impressive if the Villain were one of that large group of wrongdoers who have the technology of escalation at their disposal. One of those gangsters who defend their patch with nuclear weapons, or biological viruses, or even the venerable tactics of well-poisoning. However, this is not the case: judged against those worldly criminals, this Villain is something of a mystic. His crime, like his mathematics, is more pure than applied. He is a thief, and yet he has never shinned a pipe nor jemmied a lock, never swung swag over his shoulder, and never, never been so undignified as to have actually attended the scene of any of his crimes. He is the most theoretical of robbers, a sphinx among cat-burglars.

The Villain steals numbers. They have immense value in this place, yet they are still so public as to be unguarded. If the public were anything other than what it is — the society sump — then the Villain, stealing from it, would be a public enemy. But the fact is that the public's stigma is now so great that nobody can be moved to care about its enemies. Public transport, public toilets, public enemies, public opinion: you don't have anything to do with any of these things if you can afford not to.

This curious, undeclared enemy of the public delegates the practical business of running a crooked operation to his irregular band of cronies. The Creature of Habit catalogues the strange library of stolen numbers, and makes sure that each is kept suspended in its cocoon of magnetic isolation, utterly disconnected from the neighbouring numbers still at large in the world from which it has been torn. He can also be devastatingly annoying. Morm and the Spittlecat monitor the flow of numbers in the Metropolis to make sure the gaps don't show up too badly. And from time to time, if someone is unlucky enough to be sure that a number really has gone — unlucky enough that it was their telephone number, for example — then often it's easiest to despatch PigPog or Backstabber. Under such circumstances, they employ decidedly unmathematical methods of keeping a lid on the whole affair.

THE VALUE OF A NUMBER

There are many things you can do to a number, and as many reasons why you might want to. Add it, subtract it, cube it, expose it to all the contortions of mathematics. You could even, long ago, count things with it. But you couldn't steal it. But then again, you wouldn't have wanted to.

Times change, and there is a new mathematics of number. In the new mathematics, the digits themselves, though crucial, no longer convey the number's value. In this new order, a small four-digit number, though numerically inferior in all respects to an infinite number of numbers above it, may be much more valuable.

A PIN, for example — an access code, the power to get to wealth or credit or information — is worth many times more than the 11-digit telephone number of a pizza delivery outlet, even one that claims to use real mozzarella. The new situation is that a number's true value can no longer be separated from its place in the world.

So the new mathematics, that is, the useful mathematics, has a calculus quite different from its predecessor. It still has ordering functions, and the concept of value, but the number line has become a cloud of shifting points, tied up almost unfathomably with the world in which they exist.

And of course, it's that "almost unfathomability" which allows only a very few to learn the formulae of the new mathematics. And that, in turn, is a select group to which the Villain belongs.

Once he has stolen a number, the various values associated with it inevitably drain into his possession. Up until now, he had confined himself to the theft of large numbers. Big-digit numbers of the kind that that are lost in the babble of quantity. From time to time an account might settle on such a number or a calculation might have need of it; but an individual number that's big enough can seem pretty obscure, and isn't the kind of thing that's generally missed.

But a real earner, a high accumulator, would have to come from down among the low numbers. Obviously it couldn't be 1 or 2, or any other profound number whose absence would be noticed immediately and could even cause the whole system to hang. Better to choose an everyday number that's likely to collect value often, but isn't instrumental in the way everything meshes together. A number that no-one would ever choose because it's so unremarkable; the kind of number that a process is unlikely to settle on. A place where, as near to low as one would dare to go, a gap might most easily be overlooked.

Almost overlooked.

Despite the unblinking white lights of the Metropolis, there is still day and night. The distinction is mostly a technical one; Jiriki remembers watching the sun rise or set in the mountains. It had seemed to be a natural routine and the monks had been happy to adhere to it. But here night is the time when the Metropolis hands over a few of its hours to a few of its workers, mainly to do the ugly things it doesn't need to see: the dirt and grime is removed, ailing machines are repaired, concealed devices are serviced, the misfits can move around. And from time to time, in the subdued public places, the League of Revealers makes a hit. Normally, of course, Jiriki would not be in a situation to see such a thing; but then normally he would not be quietly escaping from the threat of years spent in comfort.

The Revealers are always well equipped with powered unfasteners and the latest in lightweight cutting gear. At a glance, they look like just another subversive guerrilla group, but they are armed with tools not weapons, and their missions shed no blood nor redistribute any wealth. It's usually all over very quickly: perhaps a smoke bomb or a flare is thrown to thwart the cameras, followed by the shrill of fast work — the abrupt hiss of the League's cog-symbol being neatly sprayed nearby by way of explanation — and a fast dispersal.

The League of Revealers: activists intent on reversing the obsession with *concealing the workings of things*, whether their protest be made by prising off chromium press-on screw covers, or stripping whole subway locomotives of their casings. At either extreme, their objectives are most widely misunderstood. There is hardly a person in the Metropolis who is not aware of their activity; but on the whole it is passed off as organised vandalism. Few are moved to question why it is that so much of the modern world must be concealed — why, in an age of scientific enlightenment, the workings must be hidden. Are the people afraid of overt function? Are modern humans so technologically advanced that they are squeamish about circuitry and ducting?

It is unhelpful to the Cause that the League itself — for reasons concerned with its own survival — is a concealed organisation.

Welcome to my home. There are plenty of people like me who live in pokes and corners. But I've got a room of my own! I like to meet people, and I get a lot of visitors. They don't stay for long, but I get so many it's probably just as well. Where do you want to go? I can take you to so many interesting places, places where people either come from or go to. My doors open on so many different landings. Do you know where to find what you're looking for? You don't? I'll take you to the Mapper! She's the one to ask if you want to find something and you don't know where it is! Location, yes, the Mapper knows all about location — it's her speciality. So come in! Mind the doors!

I'm down and out. But this is official. I think it started with a mistake; my personal record at the central dataplace got damaged somehow. I was

registered as status ... well, status something. I don't recall the figure as it had many digits, like they do. But somehow the status entry got set to null — an error in the machine, I suppose, or a power twinge, or something. It's not that I found out and changed my life accordingly; everybody's grades fluctuate with inflation and corruption as it is. No, a drop to nothing is not the kind of thing that you accept without question. But the problem is you can't get into the relevant departments to investigate the problem with the query terminals if you haven't got a grade of some sort. So here I am. I am a system error.

Look, we're here. If I've remembered right, the Mapper is through one of the doors on this level, over on the far side. Good luck!

Machines, of course, come in many shapes and sizes. Jiriki knew that already. What has surprised him most is that so many of them appear to do nothing at all, no matter how long you watch them. Some of them hum a little, but he's right to think that that alone is not a good enough reason to build one.

The humming machines are the machines of information technology. It's mainly because information itself is not a physical commodity that the machines which manipulate it are so reserved. Even those that produce — drawing onto screen or sheet — tend to do it rather discreetly. Not one of these machines will ever clank.

This is one of the features which sets them apart from the machines of other technologies. The technologies of transport, energy or manufacture lay claim to machines that make noises, smells, movement and action. The machines of information technology just make decisions.

It's a fundamental difference, one which Jiriki — because he hasn't been educated by machine — finds striking. A reasonable characteristic of most machines is that each is built to exceed, in its own specialised way, human capability: the engine which

pulls greater loads, or travels at faster speeds. So presumably these humming machines make better decisions. Well, if they do, he strongly suspects that they are keeping it to themselves.

Throughout their history, argument has raged over whether or not such machines are actually intelligent. It has been a philosophical, not a practical, debate. That the machines were making decisions which affected the real world at all was far more significant than whether they were being intelligent about it.

Fortunately, the debate is now deemed to be closed, since machines can now apply proven reasoning techniques to any problem they are posed. So, inevitably, the machines were asked to decide: *do machines think?* The answer, all things considered, was "No".

Unfortunately, that answer is not quite qualified. The machines, if they had been encouraged to analyse the problem themselves, would also have expected to be asked: *do humans think?*

The answer, all things considered, would probably have been "No".

FITTER

There is no memorial to the first human worker who was superseded by a machine. The significance of events like these at the time tends to be easily overlooked. Of course, in those days, it was too early to expect the machines to notice either.

Now, in the Metropolis, the word "automatic" is too common to be useful. Jiriki finds it a little strange that people should displace themselves with machinery — there is no device here that has not been invited. And watching the engineer, or repairer, or whatever, at work, it seems so much less complicated that he had expected.

It is understandable that he should be mistaken, because the engineer did arrive with a single part, and when the machine indicated that it was ready, he opened the panels up and, despite the bewildering complexity of the workings thus revealed, he substituted it for a seemingly identical part as easily as changing the head of a broom.

When he is a little more familiar with machines like these, Jiriki will realise that the diagnosis and repair of faults is, indeed, very complex. So complex, in fact, that most of it has been taken out of human hands. Here he has seen the end of the process: the machine has already detected a fault, diagnosed the problem, ordered the replacement part, paid for it with its own credit, and summoned the engineer. Humans are, after all, extremely versatile fitters. It is already running tests on the replacement.

Presumably, it only seems odd to Jiriki because he is a stranger here. At the monastery, the relationship between humans and machines is still one in which it is the machines which are the tools.

THE CONVINCER

No, I'm not the Mapper. I am the Convincer. You want to know what that means? OK, I'll tell you; after all, explaining is something of a speciality of mine. I am the unforeseen by-product of foolproof machines. I convince machines that their human operators did indeed mean to issue the commands which they issued.

Most modern machines, you see, make allowances for human error. This is as it should be — after all, Automated System Analysis of automated systems has shown that the most common function of a human in any system is that of Introducer of Errors. That's why today's machines are made to be foolproof. They look out for mistakes, they notice when you are going wrong. If you try to do something which seems a little contrary to what the machine was expecting, it will alert you to the error of your ways, and steer you back to how things ought to be done.

The result of this is a dramatic fall in the number of errors made by human operators.

Things get done, properly. Everything is fine. Except, however, when somebody really does want to behave rashly, when they do need to destroy all this information, or modify these usually unalterable figures. And that is when they have to call for the Convincer.

It's usually a slow process, but I have professional patience. I convince the machine that this time it really isn't a mistake. I reason out the reasons. I explain all the explanations. It can take several days until, eventually, the machine accepts that the unexpected instructions at which it had balked are not at odds with the operator's requirement. And, finally, it agrees to obey them.

These are not disobedient machines. They are obedient, foolproof machines — that is, they have been instructed to disobey the instructions of fools. The trouble for the rest of us is that sometimes it can be very hard to tell the difference.

THE BLACKBOXMAN

There's no special size for blackboxes, provided that they are big enough to contain what people put in them. There's no particular shape, either, but I like to work with three pairs of rectangular sides (one for each dimension). And there's no preferred material, so long as whatever is used is thoroughly opaque and more or less impenetrable.

You have to understand that only fools are still interested in the tiresome details! People who wonder how something works are missing the point. What is important is *what* it does, not *how* it does it. So I protect people from the unnecessary complication by putting all the workings into a blackbox. You have inputs, you have outputs, and that is enough.

You must realise that there are limits to the complexity that a human mind can tolerate. Without blackboxing, our designs could never have exceeded those limits. But they did, and we should be grateful, for now we have built a complex world that serves us. We can achieve anything, because we are no longer held back by the need to know how. So we can perform magic.

Don't think that this approach is restricted to mechanics or electronics. That's not it, that's not it at all. No; I have built blackboxes for methods, procedures, systems and whole organisations. And my work goes on, because these blackboxes can themselves be blackboxed. I'll never be finished. But day by day I keep up the struggle to keep at bay the complexity that forever threatens to choke us all.

Unfortunately for the technohistorians, the development of machines is not one with clearly defined boundaries. For example, it's not easy to pinpoint exactly when humans became dependent on their machines. Or when machines first began to take advantage of the situation. Nonetheless, there can be little doubt that these things did occur, and in that order. Furthermore, it is known that, somewhere between the two, motivation automation crept in. It marks the boundary between machines that required humans to instruct them to take over their lives, and those that did not.

Of course, it's important to realise that only a minority of machines ever benefited from the change; but that minority was nonetheless a significant one. Machines had traditionally been predictable, obedient entities that did what they were told. And, perhaps more to the point, they would keep following those instructions until told to stop, whereupon they would wait patiently for the next suggestion. What they lacked was self-motivation. Now, things are a little different, and there are machines that are quite capable of keeping themselves occupied without help from anybody.

Perhaps the first machines to be programmed to set out their own tasks were in the research labs. Research is often a repetitive and exhaustive process, something which is well within the grasp of the right sort of machines. The right sort of machines were built, and encouraged to conduct research, design and perform the necessary experiments, analyse the results, and follow up any new leads or possibilities. An ongoing task, and one that the machines turned out to be thoroughly good at.

The first problems this sort of mechanised initiative caused were deceptively mild. In fact, the problem of cybernethics is technology's very own vacuum-packed tin of metallic worms. Could a scientist (human) take credit for discoveries made by a machine, when his or her only contribution was to turn it on? Naturally, most did; on the face of it, these were just people indulging in superfluous pride and vanity. Then, soon afterwards, came the inevitable variation: could a scientist (human) be held responsible for the results of the advances made by his or her machine? And now: can machines patent their discoveries? Can they sue humans who steal their ideas? Can humans trust machines not to withhold information? Can they torture them to get at the truth?

If you're just watching me to see what's going on, then you're not getting the full picture.

Machines need to communicate with me clearly, and that's not always easy. For a start, there's always a lot happening on the screen — words and pictures flashing up here, there and everywhere ... there are bells and whistles — noises to alert me to the things I ought to know about, as and when they happen. It can all be quite bewildering and distracting, both to me and everybody around. It's better for machines to communicate more directly and more privately.

So I have a small electronic taste-bud stimulator in my mouth. Any machine can transmit a signal to it which results in one of a number of characteristic tastes. It doesn't interfere with the already overloaded screen, and it doesn't bother the neighbouring people or machines. In fact, it's very discreet (I had a tooth removed and the stimulator just slotted into its place).

Also, the fine electrodes running down the back of these skin gloves press into each finger. The keyboard can send a suggestive pulse to the right finger to encourage me to press the right button. It greatly speeds my text-typing because the machine can predict quite accurately the word I want, before I've even decided myself! The severity of the twinge varies according to the urgency with which the key must be pressed.

For really important messages, patterns can be patched directly onto my retina via these discreet receivers. This is particularly effective, because — regardless of what I'm focusing on or where I'm looking, eyes open or closed — there it is, superimposed bright and clear, in full searing colour. The installation required a tiny bit of integrated surgery on the back of my eyes and some drilling for the wires, but it's an excellent attribute to be able to offer an employer.

The wonderful thing is that the transmitters have been configured so that information can be sent to me instantly, wherever I am and whatever I may be doing — awake or asleep. So there's not the slightest possibility that I'll miss anything. If a machine has something to tell me, it can't fail to get my attention. Wonderful!

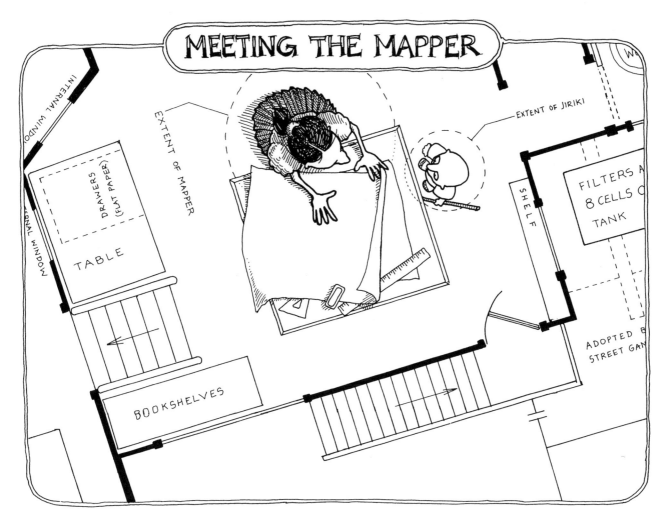

Labels within the illustration: INTERNAL WINDOW · EXTENT OF MAPPER · EXTENT OF JIRIKI · DRAWERS (FLAT PAPER) · TABLE · ···NAL WINDOW · SHELF · FILTERS A··· 8 CELLS ··· TANK · BOOKSHELVES · ADOPTED ··· STREET GAN···

"You Are Here," so this is where you can start. This is where I make my maps. I'm currently working on a commission for the sewer-rats: a map of part of the Metropolis above them. It's a tricky one: do streets change all my lefts and rights when mapped from underneath?

A 1:1 replica is the best kind of map — no loss of information. But sadly, that's often impractical. So a miniature scale model is not a bad alternative. People look at it in the same way that, from a distance, they might look at the genuine article. That's good — they can understand immediately how to use it. But people like their maps flat. So, I build up a scale model in my imagination, intricately and accurately, and then squash it flat, and draw what's left on paper. It's their loss; I build in three dimensions but they only want two. You see, mapping has been reduced down to the business of reducing things down. I'm always mapping something onto something less. Three dimensions onto two. A wall of bricks into one thin line. A whole population into a single number. It seems everything has to be condensed.

It started long ago, with mechanical and electrical things. Now it's information itself. This world, and it used to be a big world, has been completely mapped even though parts of it have never been imagined, intricately or accurately, by anyone. Satellite cameras squash the whole thing flat automatically.

But you — you want to find a book, and I don't often find myself marking the position of books on my maps. I suppose there aren't that many around any more. But I remember a bookshop, with books in it, yes, with pages which you can pinch between your fingers, and bindings which fall open at the places where previous readers have lingered the most ... yes I liked it in there, although the neighbourhood did try to have it boarded up, attracted the wrong sort of unmodern people, hanging around doing nothing but loitering with open books in their hands. Anyway, that's as good a place as any to look for a book! It's easy to find: here, I can sketch you a map.

Imagine a land where people are afraid of dragons. It is a reasonable fear: dragons possess a number of qualities that make being afraid of them a very commendable response. Things like their terrible size, their ability to spout fire, or to crack boulders into splinters with their massive talons. In fact, the only terrifying quality that dragons do not possess is that of existence.

Now, the people of this land know about dragons because their leaders have warned them about them. They tell stories about cruel dragons with razor teeth and fiery breath. They recount legends of dragons hunting by night on silent wings. In short, the leaders make sure that the people believe in all the qualities of dragons, including that key quality of existence. And then they control the people — when they need to — with their fear of dragons. The people pay a dragon-slaying tax ... everyone stays indoors after dark to avoid being snatched by swooping claws ... and nobody ever strays out of bounds for fear of being eaten well and truly up.

Perhaps somebody will wonder if dragons aren't, after all, fictitious because — despite their size — nobody seems to have actually *seen* one. And so it is necessary from time to time to provide evidence: a burnt tree or two, a splintered rock, the mysterious absence of a villager. The population is controlled by the dragons in its collective mind. It's contrived superstition, and it is possible because the people do not know enough about the way the world works to know that dragons do not exist.

Now we live in this Metropolis, and the mind dragons have been replaced by technology. We too have become a population that once again does not know enough about the way the world works. What can technology do? What are its limits? Can machines foresee things other than the weather? Are there machines that can control your thoughts? Don't underestimate the power that people who understand these things have at their disposal. I hope you can trust them.

Only this is worse, because high technology does exist — we simply don't realise that we've lost track of where its capability stops and superstition takes over. Furthermore, unlike dragons, technology is not something people expect to be able to see. The circumstantial evidence is there: lots of unfathomable machinery with invisible abilities.

People who are afraid of dragons console themselves with tales of heroic dragon-slayers. Technology offers no such saviours. This is why its hold over society is invulnerable, and the superstitions it creates are more powerful than any that have gone before.

A book says *Read Me*. It communicates that it is trying to communicate, simply by its very existence. Not like a screen that burns energy trying to attract your attention to its volatile writing, which most of the time stays hidden inside boxes, coded in the modern invisible ink of electricity and magnetism.

You should think about the duality of the physical book and its ethereal, textual contents — yes! the body/soul dichotomy of bookkind! What is it that bonds these two things so closely: the meaning that forms in your head, against the paper you can feel, really feel, in your hand? It is the power of order: the powerful, primitive rule of a series: one thing after another, in order, from beginning to end. It's true for the letters in words, the words in sentences, the sentences in text. And also the pages. They share with each other the common form of series. Every book relies on this: reorder the pages of a novel, or shuffle the pages of a dictionary, and you destroy the book. Despite this, few books ever admit to their physical form. Usually a small dot of ink, a ., conveys more information than the turn of the page, or its length or breadth, or the thickness or scent of its paper.

And the marks, those ink-symbols, are the regimented fingerprints of a typesetting machine whose inky hands hold the author and reader a respectable distance apart. It's rare to find a book in which the reader is allowed to look directly upon the marks that the author made, rather than the machine's translation in sanitised print.

But a book *could* involve its contents with its physical form. Such a book could acknowledge rather than ignore its page-breaks. It could duplicate the author's own handwriting. It could let you move from one page to the next, from beginning to end; or it could put page-numbers in the illustrations inviting you to jump to related pages. It could be missing the page between twenty-eight and thirty (stolen by its villain). It could even, five eighths of the way through, try to attract your attention to itself.

Jiriki, I'm sorry that you can't find the book you're looking for. You're welcome to browse, but that won't help if you don't know its title or even what's in it. If it's information you need, go and make a withdrawal at the databank.

There is a theory of relativity concerning failure and success. All modern judgements of human worth are made relatively. The population exists simply to provide a comparison against which to judge the individual. It is not a State, or a Greater Whole, it is simply a library of comparisons. And since the modern individual's concern is with superiority, such a collection has a name. It is "the Competition".

There are two ways of judging a human's ability: absolutely, or relatively. An absolute judgement would be something like: can I run fast? *Yes I can*, or *No I can't*. But a modern relative judgement would be: can I run the fastest? The problem with absolute judgements is that they incorporate the difficulty of definition: if I can get up to a lumbering lope, is that running fast? But relative judgements, provided that you have the competition against which to be judged, are easily made because they are self-evident. Have a running race, and the first one through the tape is the fastest. It's the clarity of the result — the lack of effort in making the decision — that has made competition the judge of these modern lives. They don't have to consider anything: competition produces a winner, at no computational cost, with no headaches.

But competition does much more than just produce a winner. The competitions of modern life, the credit ratings, the statuses, the possessions, are all Open Championships, and everybody is entered into each and every event. Producing a winner is a minority effect. Competition on this scale is simply the mass-production of losers. And remember that there can be, by definition, only one winner, regardless of the size of the population from which the winner is to emerge. The numerical significance of a single winner dwindles as the population increases. The Metropolis has a massive population engaged in competitive society. It is, therefore, a society of born losers.

There is a corollary to this theory, which explains the spread and dominance of machines in the modern world. The society of machines, which is superimposed on the society of humans, is not a competitive one. Technology has succeeded where humanity has not because there is not one machine that wastes so much as half a nanosecond of processor-time wondering if it's performing better or worse than any of the other machines around it.

One ancient truth which technology has always been unable to allow for is the incalculable ineptitude of some of its users. Take, for example, a simple device like a hammer — no complicated user interface there, no abstract conceptual model of its operation, no instruction manual to ignore — and think "thumb".

Unfortunately, as technology advances, the risks associated with it advance step for step in equal measure. From hammers to nuclear power stations; from thumbs to populations. And people are aware of this: they coined the term "failsafe" and built it into some of the systems they were nervous about.

But what *failsafe* really means here is humanproof. With a little reflection, it seems as if machines are trying to communicate something

profound back to their creators: the failsafe part of any system is where the machine knows and acts better than its operator. Failsafe means that, when it really matters, the humans can be stopped from meddling.

And there, of course, is the problem. The humility of being controlled by your own creation is one which humankind is not willing to tolerate. So from the minds that brought you "failsafe" comes "override", and people, thumbs and all, are back at risk. You use a machine and suffer the consequences. You try to launch an intimidating shriek-grenade with the safety plug still in the end of your barrel, and your equipment will explode.

Casualties like this one are systems in need of repair — usually urgently. The first tests run on any arrival here are just to discern, quickly, whether the casualty requires mechanical or medical attention. The basic principles are more or less the same — surgery is just as fiddly in either case — but I prefer medical for purely selfish reasons. There aren't as many things inside a human being that give you a jolt if you touch them with an uninsulated scalpel.

Sometimes, very occasionally, we have an Alive that has grafted in so much machinery that they get sent to mechanical. It's sad, but we don't have the time to run extensive tests. But now it's getting more common for a machine to be sent through to medical by mistake. Don't think this is a question of blood or organic tissue; for a number of reasons these are no longer reliable indicators.

The problem is this: there is no symptom of human life that cannot be *convincingly* simulated by machine. And the most acute symptom of life is consciousness. Now of course my own consciousness is something I experience personally — that's what it is, after all — so I know I'm alive. It's the rest of the world I need to decide about.

And I do mean "convincingly". You can assure me that you feel and experience life as surely as I do. You might convince me. A sufficiently sophisticated machine, however, can be equally convincing — not just in its argument, but also in the demonstration of its experience. I've observed machines behaving with apparent pain, fear, affection, even boredom. But observation only ever provides circumstantial evidence of experience. Perhaps consciousness could be communicated directly through empathy or art ... but certainly not with the definitive forms of communication — language, logic, geometry, science. Yet these, of course, are the very forms to which the machines are restricted.

Well, perhaps you think that you can be more convincing to me than a machine because you are made of the same stuff, you have more or less the same chemicals in the same kind of brain. No. Trying to reduce physical consciousness to its physical components doesn't deny machines theirs. It just means that theirs tastes a little more metallic.

I have come to conclude that the only significant difference between humans and machines is that humans are alive. Alive is a quality which has no discernible function: why should it have? It is merely, or tremendously, a quality whose only role is that of being a quality.

While you are in the Metropolis, Jiriki, notice this: the only soft things that seem to be left are foam rubber, pneumatic tyres, and human beings.

The rest of the Metropolis is hard. Much harder than it needs to be. Of course it contains things — functional things — that ought to be hard. But modern humans surround themselves with more hardness than they could possibly need. It is total. The Metropolis is full of exaggerated hardness: huge, sharp corners on and in the buildings, gleaming expanses of walls or floors, ruthlessly straight edges and unassailably right right-angles. Why is this? It is because all these things are monuments to human capability. They are all clearly, starkly deliberate; these strong, hard things have been made this way, by us. This isn't the wild: everywhere you look, there is confirmation that the conquering humans are in control. Very reassuring.

Anyway, there is an obvious drawback to having these soft, human bodies in this hard, unyielding environment. People get damaged. Since diseases can, by and large, be easily dealt with, casualty has become medicine's major field. So they work on preventative surgery. That is, preventative surgery against injury. They can go some way to hardening the soft human. They graft lightweight exoskeletons onto bodies. The materials used are light but very strong, often with heat-resistant, acid-proof and electrically insulating qualities thrown in for good measure. Sometimes discrete mechanisms are even included to power-assist the joints.

The exosurgeons can hardly keep up with the demand. So the data from their experience has been passed over to the genetic experts; instead of standing around a mature body doing hard grafts, the surgeons would prefer to see people growing their own. It's the application of preventative genetics. Harmless hardness.

Then that just leaves the foam rubber and pneumatic tyres.

People no longer notice the machines by which they are surrounded. This is a loss: there are things that even we, their creators, could learn from them. I can give you an important example. Machines are deterministic and determined — they possess a willingness to follow a rigid method without deviation or distraction. They can solve problems methodically ... but not all problems. There are things we humans overcome which machines do not begin to reason about. On the other hand, humans are intuitive — we can solve problems unmethodically ... but not all problems. When our erratic or inspirational attempts to solve them fail, we should learn from the methodical machines. We could resolve more human problems by acting less like humans.

Here is a method for the settlement of dispute between two humans, A and B. It has four steps, which must be followed without deviation or distraction.

1: A and B agree to resolve the dispute. (This is not a trivial step. It requires that a dispute does exist and that its settlement is indeed wanted.)

2: A argues B's case, questioned by B until B is convinced that A can represent B's side.

3: Step 2 is repeated with the roles reversed.

4: Then and only then do A and B demonstrate the false reasoning and unreasonable values they had to adopt in order to uphold the other's argument.

There! It's a method of solution, a program for humans. All you need to settle a dispute is to follow it. But as yet, I've not found any disputers who are willing to see it through. It seems that — even though it is impossible to choose between two things when you only have insight into one of them — they prefer the customary method of trying to convince by impressing their point of view upon the other. They are afraid that being able to argue the other point of view convincingly (with all the false reasoning that may entail) somehow demonstrates a weakness in their own.

It is all very odd. The power of intellect is that it can imagine different worlds with different rationales. It can consider different ways of considering. But, instead, people have learnt to reason unreasonably, to argue inconsiderately. Somewhere along the line, somebody must have convinced them that there is a point of view so correct that it makes any questioning redundant; a thing called *opinion*. And now everybody thinks they've got one.

INFORMATION

Jiriki can feel real power here: it is the power of information. He can sense it, feel it, taste it: never before has he felt such potential. The details of the population, their records, the results of surveillance, reports, observations, scientific knowledge, discoveries, facts and results, along with the most important element of all, the connections between them: these things are all here, available and waiting: waiting with the same silent tension with which water waits behind a towering dam. He wonders briefly if it's approaching some limit, when even all the circuits and devices of the modern Metropolis will no longer be enough to restrain it. He wonders what becomes of a society when its data bursts its banks.

All the answers are here, information is at his disposal. And no sooner wondered than known, here's an answer: data doesn't exert accumulating pressure, and technology doesn't explode if it has too much to remember.

Well, that was impressive. If technology can produce answers so very easily, could it be that humanity is nearing the end of its pursuit of knowledge? And of course, no sooner does he wonder this, than the answer is there before him. Technology, it announces, has tamed information: the pursuit of knowledge is over, because it no longer runs away.

Alas, information retrieval can never be quite what it seems. You should try asking such a

system things like: is the information with which I am being provided contradictory? Or misleading? Or biased, inaccurate or untrue? If you get a "Yes" then it becomes somewhat worthless. Alternatively, if you get a "No", you either have access to the impossible Database of Universal Truth, or — more likely — a machine that is willing to lie to you.

Information retrieval used to be a service invoked by humans. But technology has advanced enough to be able to judge, after a little analysis, what a human needs to know. Hence machines like this one, which no longer wait to be asked.

So before he can ask about the book, Jiriki is told about the Villain who stole the number whose loss the girl had been unfortunate enough to discover. He is supplied with machine-generated accounts from three angles of her abduction. He sees transcripts of her subsequent and ongoing questioning, wherein she is asked to nominate those others whose attention she may have drawn to the aberration the theft has caused. He is even given directions and plans of the Villain's base, where she is being held, in among the vaults that hold the stolen numbers in their peculiar stasis of mathematical isolation. And then he is shown a number of things, disturbing and confusing things, about the Villain and the Metropolis which are really nothing to do with him at all. Information is flowing into him thick and fast. It's time to get out of the chair and leave this particular machine behind.

It's a common mistake to assume that the purpose of a building's security system is to prevent anybody getting in. This is not the case. It is the paradox of security that most owners want their buildings to be selectively impregnable — that is, the difficulty encountered on trying to enter should depend on who it is trying to do the entering. For the design of secure buildings this paradox is a dilemma — either you let people in, or you don't — and often the best response to a dilemma is to avoid it. And buildings can avoid it, by concentrating more on monitoring intruders than preventing them from intruding. Then, if the owner (or building) so decides, getting *out* becomes the problem. There are some buildings that prefer to be selectively impregnable from the inside.

The Villain's base is such a building. Jiriki's technical naivety, which denies him the cluttering concerns of technological detail, could have overcome the problem of getting into it in a number of ways. He used one of the simplest; a door round

the back. Thereafter, finding the girl was not too difficult; he moves, not furtively, but with the confidence of one who knows where he's going. The cameras do see him, and watch him, but without a sense of alarm, because none of their furtiveness-detectors are triggered.

Then he releases the girl, and she crouches ready to scurry out; and right away the system adopts an attitude considerably more alarmed than in the moments before. They will be able to make an escape, not just because the Villain's crew are not as ready as they might have been, but because the intruder took the precaution of removing the small door through which he entered, and through which both he and the girl will leave. The building, the intelligent building, would very much have liked to slam that particular door shut. But its selective impregnability is temporarily compromised because no amount of electrical intent, no matter how urgent, can put a door back on its hinges, although the system does slavishly try.

As Jiriki runs past these unusual machines, the startling noise of gunfire is replaced by a welcome absence of shooting. The initial spatter of bullets screeches and skims off the metalwork, before the firing is halted by PigPog's barked command; even the limited imagination of a henchman can speculate on the unfavourable reaction of fracturing one of these devices with a stray shot.

Within each metal belly is one of the Villain's stolen numbers: held suspended in a cat's cradle of forces and shrouded in a skein of the most impenetrable theory. Within each one, the forces cancel each other out with the electrical unease of storms brewing without hope of the relief of discharge. Once the Villain has taken the trouble to take a number out of circulation, he does not expect to let it seep back in. (And besides, it's generally considered calamitous, when releasing numbers back into the wild, to do so in anything but the order in which they were primally induced.) So, a tremendous amount of energy is focused into these machines. Tremendous because that is the overhead of generating sufficient power to oppose the mighty forces of Universal Order, and to keep the omniscient pull of mathematics at bay. That itself is part of a more general observation that whenever humans invoke the powerful forces of science to bend the world into a shape they arrogantly and selfishly prefer, all they are ever really doing is making things more risky for themselves. When the unnatural plans of men and women unwind — which they all must do — the sheer amount of trouble that they stored up for themselves never fails to surprise them.

The practical implications of this, for one brief moment, overshadow all the philosophical ones: one stray bullet, winging unluckily into the machinework and upsetting the balance, could destroy not just the Villain's personal interests in this sector of the Metropolis, but, indeed, the sector itself, to say nothing of the following sixteen pages. So if anyone is going to be shot, it is not going to happen on this page.

Courage is a strange thing, a quality whose use is so strongly constrained by circumstance. Jiriki would die here, for the girl, or for any friend, if that is what the moment required. To be given the chance, the instant and uncomplicated chance, to be courageous is a kind event for those who would take it. But there is neither kindness nor cruelty in time, and events happen without consideration for those who have a preference. So Jiriki hears the shot just as he leaps — he *knows*, in that instant, that both he and the bullet are prohibited any change of course,

and that when his feet touch the ground and he is reunited with his alternatives, the girl will be dying.

He will be sad, after he evades his pursuers, sad for the loss of the girl, sad that she has stopped living. And he will be sad that the world could put such an unfair price on his enlightenment of moment. It is a little tragedy that after stubbornly failing to awaken to all the instantaneous yells, slaps and silences of his Abbot, it is with such a costly shot that he learns what a moment is really like.

KILLING MACHINES

The original premise for the existence of machinery — namely, to be beneficial to humans — has long since been forgotten. But it was never a very successful premise: nothing, however harmless, will ever be beneficial to everyone. People's interests, like liquids in a vessel, fill every possibility. If you invent a plate which levitates one inch above the table, somebody somewhere who used to make tablemats will start to dislike you. So the benefit brought by any given machine is bound to be selective.

The killing machines, however, are a very special case. Ultimately, the existence of any killing machines is beneficial to no one. Perhaps in the short term they serve their makers, or the society they protect, or the property of the society they protect. But for the taking of life to have become the function of any machine is not a beneficial advance.

This is not because being killed is necessarily a bad experience for the individual — although, more often than not it surely is. The problem with the killing machines is that in the modern world of humans and machines, death is the leveller. Now that machines can be as least as functionally capable as humans, the line between having and not having life has become especially significant.

If there was one thing which was to be forbidden to machines, it ought to have been crossing this boundary. And yet the killing machines are built, and they are among the most sophisticated, ingenious and expensive machines in the world. It is odd that life, ephemeral and intangible, should be so vulnerable to the invariably physical effects of machines. There is no subtle extraction or isolation of life: the killing machines only ever need to be physically destructive to be spiritually destructive. They don't need to identify the essence of life, or to trace any of the silvery, mysterious threads which may bind the spirit to the body. Or the fragile tendrils of the soul. Or whatever it all is. They just need to know that if they damage the body badly enough, the rest goes too.

Ah, Jiriki — good, you made it to the show. Step this way and see what you think. See if you can tell me what this audience is applauding.

I am producing effects that are close to those that high technology has made commonplace — things move of their own accord, objects seem to vanish and reappear, events happen at the point of a finger or the word of command ... the sort of things that happen in the everyday lives of these people day after day. Why don't they find magic remarkable then?

Perhaps they are entertained by seeing how closely I can imitate technology. That would be odd, you know — generations ago, mechanical automata were being applauded here for imitating humans.

Or perhaps they are applauding my skill. Not because it's particularly good — you can be the judge of that — but because I have a skill at all. Those same generations ago, every member of the audience would have had at least one skill — it used to be a necessity for livelihood. Now there

are people watching me who have never practiced anything. And why should they? The world's need for skillfulness has been replaced with the need to know how to operate skilful machines.

Or could it be that they are applauding simply because this is entertainment and they need no other reason? Is clapping the nervous reaction of people with too much time on their hands, trying to clear it off, like beating dust from a rug?

Whatever you think, one thing is certain: they do not know why they are applauding. These people have been over-exposed to unexplained mystery — they can no longer explain most of the things which happen around them. You should try asking them to explain electricity, or remote controls, or video recorders.

Cause and effect has been stretched into an invisible, tenuous thread. And this makes magic basically pointless. What place is there for mystery before an audience that doesn't understand anything any more?

There's a disconcerting thing about magicians: they tend not to give anything away, least of all what they're thinking. They talk about many things, the stars, the cards you could have picked, the nature of magic performed before technologically–uninformed audiences, and all the while they may be doing something else. It's as if they thought that you could be distracted with something as simple as words themselves.

For example, between the end of the preceding page and the start of this one, Jiriki was helped, without need of asking, on his way. He passed through various sliding panels and shifting compartments and even now is letting his eyes adjust to the Underneath: a strata of machine history that most people assume lies crushed under the weight of progress, when in fact parts of it exist most surely, in the unmapped interface corridors of the Extreme Machine. Meanwhile, above, the wizard drops the curtains before his audience, muffling their applause with a velvet barrier, and turns with incoincidently perfect timing to greet, with just the appropriate amount of alarm, the Villain's cronies as they burst onto the stage from which Jiriki vanished.

They want to find a single, unmistakable trapdoor, in the position where the cabinet stood when Jiriki slipped into it, but the more they look the more trapdoors they find, and the more useless the search becomes. The magician helpfully reveals an unending succession of intricate hairline joins and secret hinges; yet all the while, the more doors and panels he provides, the more impossible the significant one becomes to distinguish. He can shuffle possibilities as smoothly as cards in a pack, all the time behaving so normally, so unexceptionally, that there is never the slightest suspicion of deceit. It is because of this most unruffled of allies that, of all the things Jiriki may care to be concerned about, the risk of getting caught is no longer one of them.

As Jiriki looks around him, and sees the strange, dusty interface tunnels of the Extreme Machine, he knows he's lost. Oddly enough, he finds it safe and reassuring. He's been lost ever since he arrived in the Metropolis, of course, but being simply lost in tunnels seems a welcome relief to being lost in all the confusing and senseless bewilderment which is the Metropolis.

Part of being an outsider is not knowing how a place or society works. In the monastery, he knew what was what — he knew whose turn it was to sweep the steps, or which bowl in the kitchen was for heating soup, and which for boiling water. Here in the Metropolis he doesn't know where anybody belongs, or how it all works, or why it's supposed to matter. He is well and truly lost.

But actually, he is not alone in this. Certainly, life-long inhabitants of the Metropolis can get the right kind of drug from a digital self-service pharmacological dispensary, or use a flavour pellet and thermocard to make a warm and tasty drink, but the truth is that they, too, have no real idea of how any of this works. They live their lives with the rituals that get them through the maze of systems and numbers and people and rights and rules that they have woven about themselves, but none of them have any real grasp of which way they are going or where in it they really are.

Perhaps everybody here is lost, but unlike the others Jiriki is simple enough to know it.

THE HUMAN BEING MACHINE

When Jiriki meets the Human Being Machine, it does not speak for itself —although it could — so the narrative must speak for it instead. It was inevitable that a machine would be built which was based extensively on the design of human beings. Despite the overwhelming arguments against things like an inherently unstable bipedal posture or forward-only binocular vision, it had to be and here it is.

The machine is regarded by some of those involved in its construction as something of a masterpiece. Perhaps that is as it should be; it's a very complicated piece of machinery with remarkable engineering.

The technicians who designed the Human Being Machine, however, found themselves involved in a project that made demands on their skills like none they had ever faced before. Time and time again they found that their devices performed beyond the acceptable limits; often too precise, or too strong, or too fast — and always too predictable.

The Human Being Machine, for example, is right-handed. This is difficult for a machine. It has to distort all its own control signals so its limbs and fingers behave imperfectly. It can then learn through its own experience to allow for this artificial distortion — it is programmed to compensate more accurately on its 'favoured' side. This machine is always striving to operate below its inhuman capabilities.

All in all, a great deal of effort went into building the Human Being Machine. It is, in most respects, unquestionably close to the inspirational design. There are just one or two major items that the engineers were unable to extrapolate from the original (evolution, if that's what it is, does not supply technical design documentation). One is, still, the design of the brain: pending future enlightenment, this model uses the processor from an arcade game system, with a few connections blown. Another is what the whole thing is supposed to be for. Research into possible motivations concluded that whatever it is that human beings — and, hence, this Human Being Machine — might have been designed to do can't have been very demanding. Otherwise, such avoidable features as instability, restricted vision, imprecision, frailty and — to top it all — mortality, would never have been incorporated.

54

One of the most impressive capabilities of human beings is their ability to be aware of their surroundings. Perhaps not in a rigorous or thoroughly detailed way, but certainly when one of them breaks somebody else's window or treads on another's toe, it knows about it. These are not haphazard examples. They are the kind of events that are detected even though the attention of the creature is directed — apparently totally — elsewhere.

This is not a common characteristic among machines. If they are minded at all, they tend to be single-minded. So it is not unheard of for a paint-spraying robot arm to elbow each and every freshly-painted teapot off the conveyor belt as it moves on to spray the next. The problem is one of feedback. A lot of machines are built without nerves — they have no feedback from their perimeter; they are blind and deaf and numb to everything outside of their function.

The problem can be overcome by adding sensors to the surface area — the entire surface area — of the machine. The machine must also be provided with the means for interpreting its new sensations. And then it must be equipped with responses to the situations it is now able to detect. All these things add considerably to the complexity of the original machine. It helps, therefore, to minimise the sensors required, and the only way to do that — without leaving numb patches — is to minimise the surface area of the machine.

The result was a machine that had a thorough understanding of the things around it and was fully aware of what, at any moment, it was in contact with. It was also, due to minimal-surface-area considerations, a machine that was entirely spherical.

It could roll around a bit. But, on the whole, the machine that was built to be aware of its surroundings turned out to be only good for filling up space that would otherwise have been left undisturbed.

Coincidently, this is also one of the least impressive capabilities of many human beings.

By functional standards, here is a machine which is something of a curiosity. Although perhaps curiosity is the wrong word.

When Jiriki was learning to read and write at the monastery, his teachers made him see the letters. This has to be done young, before their shapes are muffled by familiarity. They would give him his brush, and he would paint a single letter, and watch it for the day. He had nothing to consider but the black ink and the white paper, the slow curves or abrupt angles, the fast strokes, the junctions, the points, and the sounds they represented. (He particularly recalls the day of O, which started with an exceptionally still and misty morning.) Near the end of the month, he was shown how to form the question mark: the monks told him, "this is the one which will cause you the most trouble," and they made the sounds that are associated with it, and left him to complete the exercise. He knew even then that his teachers didn't say that kind of thing unless they meant it.

So, as he looks at the Asking Machine, wandering lost in the corridors of the Extreme Machine, he is somewhat familiar with the strange concept of Question. He has already made the association between language and question — that one is really useless without the other. So he thought he knew that questions, and the desire to ask them, were a characteristically human thing. But now he wonders: can curiosity be mechanised?

It's the same kind of curiosity that led to the construction of the Asking Machine. A simple machine with a simple operation: to form a question about anything in its massive information store, ask it to a passing human, and to add the answer it receives back into that store. Of course, when the machine was built and first switched on, the store was empty except for the one small concept of question. A curiosiseed. And now, years later, it has filled that space with a mass of considered and connected information: it has found out about science, and people, and untruths, and language, and typing errors, and art. And it still analyses every element of its accumulated knowledge in order to phrase each subsequent question.

Now though the question is always more or less the same. Jiriki reads off the screen: "I still don't get it: why did you build me?"

THE PUSH OF A BUTTON

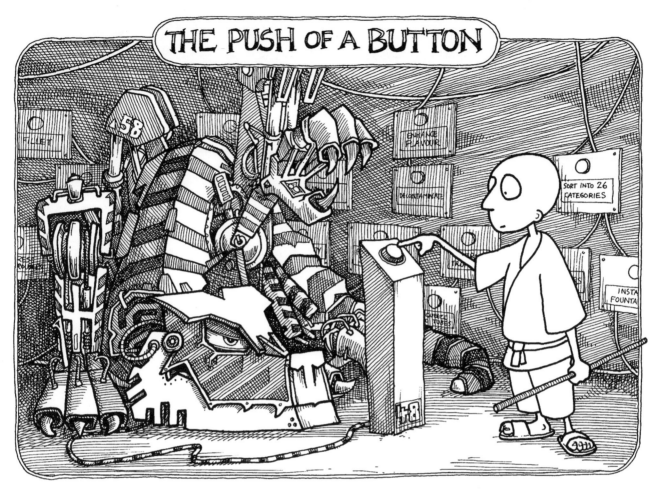

In the modern world of the Metropolis, button ought to be a verb. The vast majority of activities that are undertaken here require the pressing, pushing or prodding of at least one button. And, often, that is all.

A button is an innocuous little thing. Jiriki had imagined that the Metropolis would be infested with machines, so that the predominant articles would be things such as wheels, engines and motors. Or — to be a little more electrical — wires, switches and circuit boards. All those things are here, and it may well be an infestation. But the gutsy, machinic pieces and assemblies are relegated to the background. What predominates instead are the places where the two worlds, human and machine, touch: the keypads, consoles and buttons, touched on one side by the fingertips of human beings, on the other by the filament sensors of the altogether more awesome machines. It is a strangely delicate join.

There seems to Jiriki to be something almost disturbing about the minuscule action of pressing a button. In the Metropolis, he's seen powerful machinery brought lurching into action by such a feeble act. It reminds him of a tale the elder

monks told him once, when he was a youngster: the Last Ride of the Tiger Tickler. There was, according to fiction, a man who came upon an untended tiger cub. He took it home and raised it, and, when it was fully grown, he took to riding into town on its back. He steered the beast with a silk handkerchief: he'd lean forward and flick the tiger's left or right ear to make it turn, or brush its nose to make it start or stop. Of course, the tiger, brought up on milk and honey lapped from a bowl held in the kind man's hands, didn't know any better, so he went along with it. Disregarding the tiresome details of the tale, when the Tiger Tickler mistakenly rides into town on a different tiger, who despite similar build and markings has a radically different opinion as to the rightful place of mankind (namely in, not on), everybody gets eaten up. The silk handkerchief, under the new set of circumstances, turns out to be of no use at all.

Machines are not tigers. Nonetheless, if humans are becoming solely capable of raising their fingers, it would be bad if their circumstances were to change. They used to be able to do so much more.

THE EXTREME MACHINE

Machines, as a class, are versatile. But taken on their own, most have a restricted range of capabilities. Not so the Extreme Machine, which, when it is completed, will be capable of performing any feat. Or, at least, that is the specification to which the Extreme Machine is being built. Unfortunately, or fortunately, depending on your point of view, it is a specification which will never be met.

Jiriki won't know how the construction of this huge Extreme Machine started — or who, if anybody, was responsible for setting it off. The machines that were given the task of building it continue to do so, whilst up above them the Metropolis has forgotten all about it.

One of the difficulties is that the Extreme Machine is going to be infinitely large. This is clear now, but presumably its creator was not concerned with practicalities, and the building machines do not look ahead. For instance, the Extreme Machine, by definition, must be able to service itself. So a whole wing of the machine has been built to this end. Moreover, the Extreme Machine, by definition, must be able to service the parts that service itself. So another wing has been built onto the service wing. And then in turn ... The team of building machines assigned to the

service wing have been consistently busy since the project began; their demand for materials has not slackened, although now they are working and tunnelling several miles away from the core of the machine where they began.

Another problem which has contributed to the Extreme Machine's impending uselessness is the control room. Or rooms. The control panel, for simplicity, has one button for each of the machine's functions. This means it is easy to build and easy to use. But the Extreme Machine has — or will have — an infinite number of functions, so it also means that it is not a trivial problem finding the button you want to press. Or even which square mile you'll find it in.

So, due to a design error, the machine that can do everything is too good to be true. It is inevitable, however, that in time (if it hasn't happened already) the building machines will wire in a button which, when pressed, would design a better Extreme Machine (because the Extreme Machine, by definition, has a button for everything). It is a mechanical irony that the building machines, dutifully following their instructions to construct, will not think to press it.

In simpler times, populations could be inspired. Not just individuals, but populations. A skilled orator, or an extravagant visionary, could walk into a town square or perhaps through a city gate, and have an effect. Crowds would gather, word would spread. Perhaps such populations were gullible, or vulnerable, but if nothing else they were interested. Those were simpler times.

Now, communication is a solved problem. Not just because any number of people can disagree with each other regardless of the distance between them, but because every aspect of presentation and influence has been touched. It's all been analysed. Technology has all the ways of getting a message across. The result is an endless bombardment of messages, every one getting through in its own inevitable way. And just as the rats of the Metropolis immunised themselves by unavoidable exposure to its poisons, so the people here have become immune to communication.

It's not what the pioneers of modern communication would have predicted. They could have been forgiven for imagining that, for example, their new textdrug was going to be used to carry some momentous message directly to the consciousness of all its takers. Whereas, sadly, the chances are that those momentous messages announced the brand-name of the sweetest smelling brand of deodorant, together with — for such is the nature of commerce — equally compelling declarations from the vendors of all the other brands of the sweetest smelling deodorants.

Which is all a rather roundabout way of noticing that these modern humans are beyond inspiration. There are no great visionaries, there are no tides of opinion. And writing on the floor goes unnoticed underfoot — at least until the day some promoter discovers the worth of shoes that read to their wearers. Jiriki notices; it's an old bit of floor, and it is an historic, albeit forgotten monument to the last popular uprising in this technological world. It dates from the time when, for the last time, the people agreed on their grievances against the modern world and demanded, as oppressed people often do, changes to a bad system. But this system was too far gone to change, so what they got instead were the Five Admissions. The government, if that's what it was, was nothing if not honest.

If you had stayed up in the mountains, you would never have seen me like this. It seems better up there, where I'm not given a shape, or clothes to wear, or terror. We could not have met and talked like this — so I am pleased you were sent, and it's good to meet you.

At the monastery, death is simply when something stops living. There can be enough loss and peace and grief in that alone that the Abbots have never felt that they needed to add to it.

But here that is not enough. Here, death is where I come howling into their busy lives, wrecking with this foolish, gruesome blade; or it is when I wait and lurk in the shadows in terrible inactivity. Well, when their lives come to an end they are often emotional and confused, so perhaps they are entitled to a little visualisation.

Now it goes beyond that. They use me to scare themselves, for thrills — they actually revel in the

excitement of the fear they have wound about me. They put me in the stories they tell their children. They make me star in their sickening films. They make me play games of risk (in which I have to feel cheated if they win). And all the time they have me grin, because they imagine that if they had this kind of power, they would be enjoying it.

For all their efforts though, I am still uninterestingly simple. I am the end of lives spent shrouded in interfaces, front-ends and images; the first, only and last direct experience of something in which they are really and simply involved. And, perhaps you have noticed, simplicity is taboo here. Among all this technology, I remain the blackest box of all.

Your Abbot was a good man, Jiriki. I look forward to meeting your successor.

The world of the Metropolis, the ultimate human environment, is thoroughly contrived. Everything here, be it ugly or appealing, good or bad, is a human effect. Most of the surroundings and artefacts are truly artificial. And the remainder, maybe those made of a material that is almost natural, are constrained to human obedience in some way or another. Nothing, absolutely nothing, has been left alone. No stone, as they say, has been left unturned. Or uncarved. Or uncrushed. Or unplasticised. Thus all connections between this huge place and any natural order have been severed ... or *almost* all. There remains one fundamentally natural arrangement that has yet to be possessed and processed by human ingenuity — and that, of course, is humankind itself. So technology and medical science have been dutifully set upon this final pocket of resistance.

Once, when he was much younger, Jiriki asked the Abbot why the mountain was there. The old man did not tell him; instead, the young monk was given a bag with food in it, and sent to stand on the peak to ask the mountain why Jiriki was there. "It's the same question," the Abbot had told him, "so pay attention to the answer you get back from the mountain." He returned as night was falling, and the monks put him next to the warm fire, and he fell asleep watching the Abbot watching him through the flames. Two questions. One answer.

As he stands here in the Metropolis, without the book he was sent for, Jiriki remembers standing on the mountain straining to hear an explanation among the silence. Here, in the Metropolis, the world abounds with explanations: he could spend a lifetime straining to hear the silence among them all. Everything here has an explanation, a justification for why it exists, or who made it, or what purpose it is supposed to serve. It seems natural to people who know no other way — but the truth is that the real world, the natural world, does not affix an explanation to every item it contains. This is a human system: it is the nature of unnatural things.

The Abbot sent Jiriki to the Metropolis in exactly the same way he sent him up the mountain: to bring back an answer much less artificial than a mere explanation. Jiriki has begun to understand. Perhaps he knows where the book is, or perhaps he doesn't. Either way, he knows that his journey here is over, and it is time to return.

In the Metropolis, there are daily murders. People kill each other, and they have their reasons (not all guns, and even fewer knives, go off accidentally). In the monastery, there are no murders. The monks do not kill each other, although from time to time even they might think they have their reasons. (Monks don't find each other agreeable all the time. That would be suspiciously unreal, and monasteries are, as any monk quickly discovers, very realistic places). The absence of crime in the monastery is based on a very simple method of prevention — the monks try hard, with considerable success, to control their actions so that criminal things like stealing, or committing murder, simply never get done.

It's actually a very good solution, but it doesn't work in the Metropolis. Perhaps there was a time when it could — but now the Metropolis has a snagging complexity of its own, and all of its inhabitants are drawn as parts into the difficulties of the whole. Even Jiriki, an outsider, could not remain uninvolved — the girl did die, and he cannot forget it.

The Metropolis has developed into a working landscape of systems and machines, an environment generated by humans but not constrained by them. The modern world no longer needs its human creators, it can survive without them; the dependency is the other way round. The people here struggle to live in any way which makes them feel other than surplus to requirements. Nobody is to blame, but collectively humans surrendered control of their technology a little too readily, and brought this upon themselves.

Jiriki believes, not least because it was a theme of his Abbot's teaching, that struggling against anything is itself the cause of distress. This modern system seems to make struggling a way of life. Perhaps, like some of the quiet pools or tangled woods in the more remote parts of the wild, the Metropolis has become a place that would be better left undisturbed. Perhaps what Jiriki has been observing here is life in an otherwise satisfactory world.

COUNTING STEPS OF ONE

This far from the Metropolis, on steps which have somehow escaped the advances of escalator technology, Jiriki finally sees numbers in their natural state. Here in the wilderness numbers are free from all the associations and values with which technology burdens them: inherently, reliably simple. On reflection, it seems odd to him that such simple things should be the fundamental mechanism with which the modern world implements its encumbering complexity. There, the profundity of numbers has been completely obscured in the reckless pursuit of function.

For example, zero is a profound number because it is not arbitrary. Where there is nothing, there are zeroes. Or maybe just one, huge, all-encompassing zero. Look for something that isn't there, and zero dominates your counting so thoroughly that try as you might you cannot get beyond it. You don't count in zeroes; when you count, zero is the mute background and one is your tool.

One is a profound number, like and unlike zero, because it is not arbitrary. Out here in the wilderness, or out there in the voids of space,

there are ones. One is the symbol and the count of all existence. A unit of one, and the measure of all counting: count the steps up to a monastery, even in a casual, homecoming sort of way, and you are really giving names to recurring ones.

Two is a profound number. It is not arbitrary that existence and non-existence are a pair. Two is the sum of the universe, the simplest way of counting everything that either exists, or else doesn't.

Three is a little less profound — three is only the result of counting three things. Those things may be significant or beautiful, but nonetheless that three needs a context. It is not, strictly speaking, a universally profound number.

And four — although, like three and all the higher numbers induced from it, it is not fundamentally profound — four has a certain purity about it. Two doubled. A profound number profounded. And then so to eight, sixteen, thirty-two and sixty-four. Jiriki would have found out more, but this monastery is on a finite mountain, and the stairway doesn't quite make it to one hundred and twenty-eight.

63

The last page is the one which is followed by no other pages. It is not obliged to conclude anything except the ordering of the pages that precede it.

Of course, the contents of a page can spill over physical boundaries such as the edges of paper, or the covers of a book. That is the tremendous property of information; it has, at best, a curious relationship with its physical space. If there were ever such things as information-bombs, they would be books. They would be particularly powerful devices, because each one could go off an almost unlimited number of times. When the words are read, the release triggered, information springs out of the flat world of paper pages into an altogether more complicated place. And, like fall-out, it can persist beyond the event, after the book is closed.

The book that the Abbot has left behind for Jiriki is mostly blank. It contains a few notes and reminders, and the address of a cartoonist in the Metropolis who might be able to do the illustrations

and the lettering, when it's ready. As for the contents, well, Jiriki has discovered that sometimes choosing the contents of a book are less a matter for its author than might be supposed. Particularly when the book is about a monk's modern enlightenment, whose predecessor sent him out to collect the contents of the pages, albeit in their unwritten form.

So it is that Jiriki, having experienced the contents of a Book of Pages, will write them down. If he ever doubts that the world he remembers is real, he only has to look at the book — no doubt about it: a page is missing. So he knows that the Villain is still out there, stealing numbers, and that the modern world continues to exist, indifferent to the opinions of wandering monks. Later, the time will come when Jiriki will select one of the more promising youngsters and send him off in search of his own pages. After all, if the monastery is to continue, somebody will have to understand what it is they are rejecting after Jiriki himself is gone.

This Book of Pages is open.

The more ingenious and clever men are,
The more strange things happen.
            — Lao Tsu, over 2000 years ago

This, however, you must know:
I find that God made man simple;
man's complex problems are of his own devising.
                — the Qoheleth (Ecclesiastes), over 2000 years ago